SLYTHERIN.

RAVENCLAW.

GRYFFINDOR.

Let's All Just Keep Our

Fingers Crossed And Hope for The Best!

_____

_____

_____

_____

_____

_____

_____

_____

_____

_____

_____

_____

_____

_____

_____

_____

_____

_____

_____

SEEKER

GRYFFINDOR.

Let's All Just Keep Our

Fingers Crossed And Hope for The Best!

_____

_____

_____

_____

_____

_____

_____

_____

_____

_____

_____

_____

_____

_____

_____

_____

_____

SEEKER

GRYFFINDOR.

Let's All Just Keep Our Fingers Crossed And Hope for The Best!

_____

_____

_____

_____

_____

_____

_____

_____

_____

_____

_____

_____

_____

_____

_____

_____

_____

_____

SEEKER

GRYFFINDOR.

Let's All Just Keep Our Fingers Crossed And Hope for The Best!

_____

_____

_____

_____

_____

_____

_____

_____

_____

_____

_____

_____

_____

_____

_____

_____

SEEKER

GRYFFINDOR

Let's All Just Keep Our Fingers Crossed And Hope for The Best!

SEEKER

GRYFFINDOR.

Let's All Just Keep Our Fingers Crossed And Hope for The Best!

_____

_____

_____

_____

_____

_____

_____

_____

_____

_____

_____

_____

_____

_____

_____

_____

SEEKER

GRYFFINDOR

Let's All Just Keep Our

Fingers Crossed And Hope for The Best!

_____

_____

_____

_____

_____

_____

_____

_____

_____

_____

_____

_____

_____

_____

_____

_____

_____

_____

_____

SEEKER

PROCLAMATION.
EDUCATIONAL DECRE
No 30
NO MUSIC
IS TO BE
PLAYED
DURING
Study
Hours

PROCLAMATION.
EDUCATIONAL DECRE
No. 24
ALL STUDENT ORGANIZATI
ARE HENCEFORT
DISBANDED
Any student in
noncompliance
WILL BE
EXPELLED

PROCLAMATION.
EDUCATIONAL DECREE
No. 27
ANY STUDENT FOUND
IN POSSESSION
OF THE MAGAZINE
THE QUIBBLER
WILL BE
EXPELLED

CLAMATION.
NAL DECREE
No 29
RACURRICULAR
CTIVITIES
Are Subject to
Review by the
High Inquisitor

CLAMATION.
TIONAL DECREE
No 98
WISHING TO JOIN THE
ISITIONAL SQUAD
EXTRA CREDIT
ey sign up in the
High Inquisitor's
OFFICE

AMATION.
TIONAL DECREE
No. 82
L STUDENTS
ILL SUBMIT TO
QUESTIONING
ABOUT
Suspected
ILLICIT
Activities

SEEKER

GRYFFINDOR.

Let's All Just Keep Our

Fingers Crossed And Hope for The Best!

SEEKER

GRYFFINDOR

Let's All Just Keep Our Fingers Crossed And Hope for The Best!

_____
_____
_____
_____
_____

_____
_____
_____

_____
_____
_____

_____
_____
_____

_____
_____
_____

_____

SEEKER

_____

_____

_____

_____

_____

_____

_____

_____

_____

_____

_____

_____

_____

_____

_____

_____

_____

SEEKER

GRYFFINDOR

Let's All Just Keep Our

Fingers Crossed And Hope for The Best!

_____

_____

_____

_____

_____

_____

_____

_____

_____

_____

_____

_____

_____

_____

_____

_____

_____

SEEKER

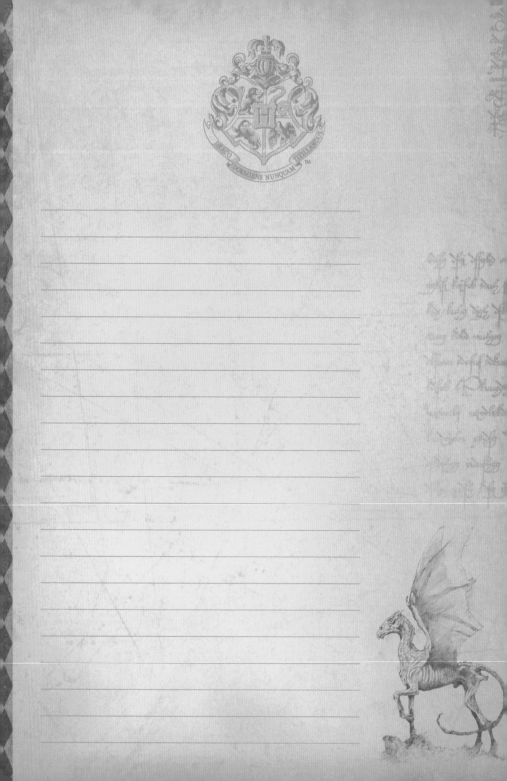

_____

_____

_____

_____

_____

_____

_____

_____

_____

_____

_____

_____

_____

_____

_____

_____

SEEKER

GRYFFINDOR

Let's All Just Keep Our Fingers Crossed And Hope for The Best!

GRYFFINDOR.

Let's All Just Keep Our
Fingers Crossed And Hope for The Best!

_____

_____

_____

_____

_____

_____

_____

_____

_____

_____

_____

_____

_____

_____

_____

SEEKER

GRYFFINDOR.

Let's All Just Keep Our

Fingers Crossed And Hope for The Best!

SEEKER

GRYFFINDOR.

Let's All Just Keep Our

Fingers Crossed And Hope for The Best!

PROCLAMATION.
EDUCATIONAL DECREE
No 30
NO MUSIC
IS TO BE
PLAYED
DURING
Study
Hours

PROCLAMATION.
EDUCATIONAL DECREE
No 29
EXTRACURRICULAR
ACTIVITIES
Are Subject to
Review by the
High Inquisitor

PROCLAMATION.
EDUCATIONAL DECREE
No 24
ALL STUDENT ORGANIZATIONS
ARE HENCEFORTH
DISBANDED
Any student in
noncompliance
WILL BE
EXPELLED

PROCLAMATION.
EDUCATIONAL DECREE
No 98
WISHING TO JOIN THE
INQUISITIONAL SQUAD
EXTRA CREDIT
May sign up in the
High Inquisitor's
OFFICE

PROCLAMATION.
EDUCATIONAL DECREE
No 27
ANY STUDENT FOUND
IN POSSESSION
OF THE MAGAZINE
THE QUIBBLER
WILL BE
EXPELLED

PROCLAMATION.
EDUCATIONAL DECREE
No 82
ALL STUDENTS
WILL SUBMIT TO
QUESTIONING
ABOUT
Suspected
ILLICIT
Activities

GRYFFINDOR.

Let's All Just Keep Our

Fingers Crossed And Hope for The Best!

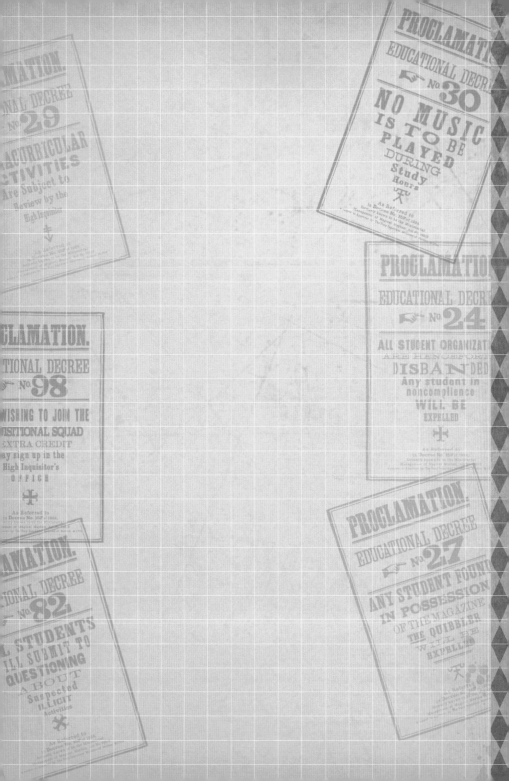

GRYFFINDOR

Let's All Just Keep Our

Fingers Crossed And Hope for The Best!

SEEKER

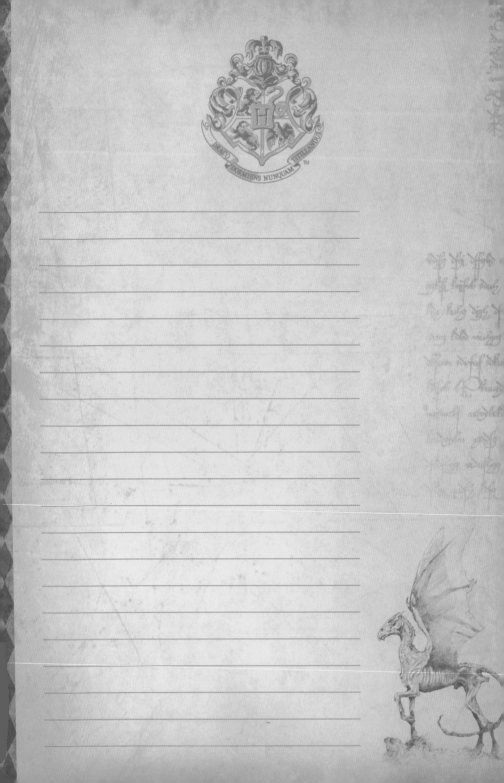

GRYFFINDOR.

Let's All Just Keep Our

Fingers Crossed And Hope for The Best!

_____

_____

_____

_____

_____

_____

_____

_____

_____

_____

_____

_____

_____

_____

_____

_____

_____

_____

SEEKER

GRYFFINDOR

Let's All Just Keep Our
Fingers Crossed And Hope for The Best!

_____
_____
_____
_____
_____
_____
_____
_____
_____
_____
_____
_____
_____
_____
_____
_____
_____
_____

SEEKER

GRYFFINDOR

Let's All Just Keep Our

Fingers Crossed And Hope for The Best!

SEEKER

PROCLAMATION.

EDUCATIONAL DECREE

☞ No. 30

NO MUSIC
IS TO BE
PLAYED
DURING
Study
Hours
⚜

As Referred to
in Decree No. 359 of 1994.

PROCLAMATION.

EDUCATIONAL DECREE

☞ No. 24

ALL STUDENT ORGANIZATI
ARE HENCEFORT
DISBANDED
Any student in
noncompliance
WILL BE
EXPELLED
✠

As Referred to
in Decree No. 359 of 1994,
formerly known to the Ministerial
Management of Magical Matters as 147F8

PROCLAMATION.

EDUCATIONAL DECREE

☞ No. 27

ANY STUDENT FOUN
IN POSSESSION
OF THE MAGAZINE
THE QUIBBLER
WILL BE
EXPELLED
⚜

As Referred to
in Decree No. 3

PROCLAMATION.

AMATION.

ONAL DECREE

No. 29

RACURRICULAR
CTIVITIES
Are Subject to
Review by the
High Inquisitor
⚓

As Referred to
in Decree No. 359 of 1994,

CLAMATION.

ATIONAL DECREE

No. 98

WISHING TO JOIN THE
UISITIONAL SQUAD
EXTRA CREDIT
May sign up in the
High Inquisitor's
OFFICE
✠

As Referred to
in Decree No. 359 of 1994.

AMATION.

TIONAL DECREE

No. 82

L STUDENTS
ILL SUBMIT TO
QUESTIONING
ABOUT
Suspected
ILLICIT
Activities
✠

As Referred to
in Decree No. 359 of 1994,

GRYFFINDOR

Let's All Just Keep Our Fingers Crossed And Hope for The Best!

SEEKER

GRYFFINDOR.

Let's All Just Keep Our Fingers Crossed And Hope for The Best!

_____

_____

_____

_____

_____

_____

_____

_____

_____

_____

_____

_____

_____

_____

_____

_____

_____

_____

SEEKER

GRYFFINDOR

Let's All Just Keep Our

Fingers Crossed And Hope for The Best!

SEEKER

GRYFFINDOR.

Let's All Just Keep Our
Fingers Crossed And Hope for The Best!

GRYFFINDOR

Let's All Just Keep Our Fingers Crossed And Hope for The Best!

SEEKER

GRYFFINDOR

Let's All Just Keep Our

Fingers Crossed And Hope for The Best!

_____
_____
_____
_____
_____
_____
_____
_____
_____
_____
_____
_____
_____
_____
_____

SEEKER

PROCLAMATION

EDUCATIONAL DECRE
No 30

NO MUSIC
IS TO BE
PLAYED
DURING
Study
Hours

...AMATION
...NAL DECREE
No 29

...ACURRICULAR
CTIVITIES
Are Subject to
Review by the
High Inquisitor

PROCLAMATION.

...ATIONAL DECREE
No 98

...WISHING TO JOIN THE
...UISITIONAL SQUAD
...EXTRA CREDIT
...ay sign up in the
High Inquisitor's
OFFICE

PROCLAMATION

EDUCATIONAL DECRE
No 24

ALL STUDENT ORGANIZATI
ARE HENCEFORT
DISBANDED
Any student in
noncompliance
WILL BE
EXPELLED

...AMATION
...TIONAL DECREE
No 82

...L STUDENTS
...ILL SUBMIT TO
QUESTIONING
ABOUT
Suspected
ILLICIT
Activities

PROCLAMATION.

EDUCATIONAL DECREE
No 27

ANY STUDENT FOUN
IN POSSESSION
OF THE MAGAZINE
THE QUIBBLER
WILL BE
EXPELLED

GRYFFINDOR

Let's All Just Keep Our
Fingers Crossed And Hope for The Best!

SEEKER

SEEKER

GRYFFINDOR

Let's All Just Keep Our Fingers Crossed And Hope for The Best!

SEEKER

GRYFFINDOR

Let's All Just Keep Our
Fingers Crossed And Hope for The Best!

SEEKER

GRYFFINDOR

Let's All Just Keep Our
Fingers Crossed And Hope for The Best!

SEEKER

GRYFFINDOR.

Let's All Just Keep Our

Fingers Crossed And Hope for The Best!

SEEKER

GRYFFINDOR.

Let's All Just Keep Our

Fingers Crossed And Hope for The Best!

_____

_____

_____

_____

_____

_____

_____

_____

_____

_____

_____

_____

_____

_____

_____

_____

_____

SEEKER

GRYFFINDOR

Let's All Just Keep Our

Fingers Crossed And Hope for The Best!

Let's All Just Keep Our
Fingers Crossed And Hope for The Best!

_____

_____

_____

_____

_____

_____

_____

_____

_____

_____

_____

_____

_____

_____

_____

_____

_____

SEEKER